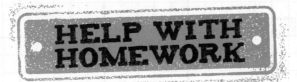

HELP WITH HOMEWORK

READING & WRITING

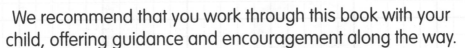

Here's a short note for parents:

We recommend that you work through this book with your child, offering guidance and encouragement along the way.

Find a quiet place to sit, preferably at a table, and encourage your child to hold their pencil correctly.

Try to work at your child's pace and avoid spending too long on any one page or activity.

Most of all, emphasise the fun element of what you are doing and enjoy yourselves. You can add a reward sticker to the bottom of each page as you complete it.

Reward sticker!

Autumn
Publishing

Alphabet blocks

Finish writing the letters of the alphabet on these blocks.
Then look at the objects. What letters do they begin with?
Draw lines to join each object to the correct letter.

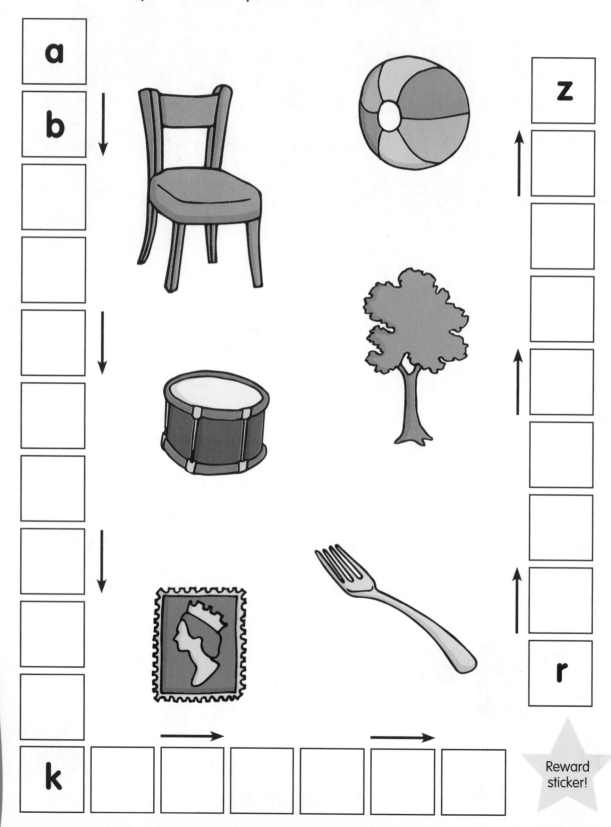

Reward sticker!

Finish the rhyme

Complete the nursery rhyme below by working out which of the words in the boxes goes in each gap.

ten   finger   four   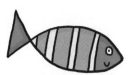go

you

One, two, three, _____ , five.

Once I caught a fish alive.

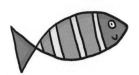

Six, seven, eight, nine, _____.

Then I let it _____ again.

Why did _____ let it go?

Because it bit my finger so.

Which _____ did it bite?

This little finger on the right.

Reward
sticker!

3

Find the vowels

Vowels are the letters **a**, **e**, **i**, **o** and **u**. Find them below and circle them. There are **25** in total.

a   t   c   t

z   f   e   v

o   i   a

o   s

u   i

b   j   o

y   u

e   w

u   u

a   e   h

m   i   i

e   n

b   o

x   a

d   a   i   u

o   g

g   e

Find the consonants

Consonants are letters that are not vowels. Find them below and circle them. There are **25** in total.

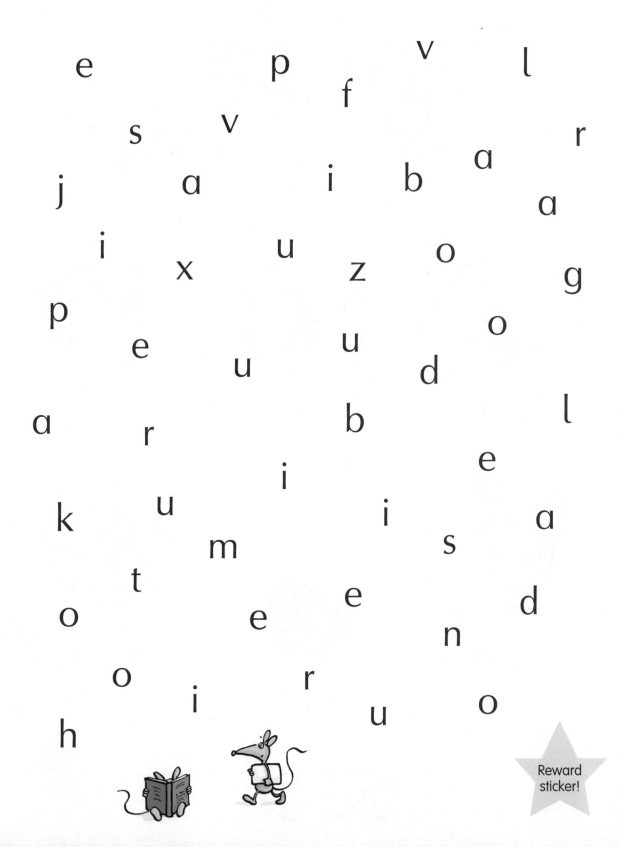

Reward sticker!

Missing vowels

Fill in the missing vowels to complete the words below.
Hint: The vowels are **a**, **e**, **i**, **o** and **u**.

c__t

b__d

f__n

d__g

m__g

h__n

n__t

b__x

k__ng

fl__g

fr__g

dr__m

sh__p

h__rp

m__st

sw__m

Missing consonants

Write the correct consonant at the start of each word.
Hint: Consonants are letters that are not vowels.

__rog

__ree

__ocket

__able

__ar

__lock

__ock

__rab

__rush

Labels

Labels can be used on pictures to help us understand the information. Write the correct labels in the empty boxes below, using these words.

neck   leg   horn   ear   hoof   tail

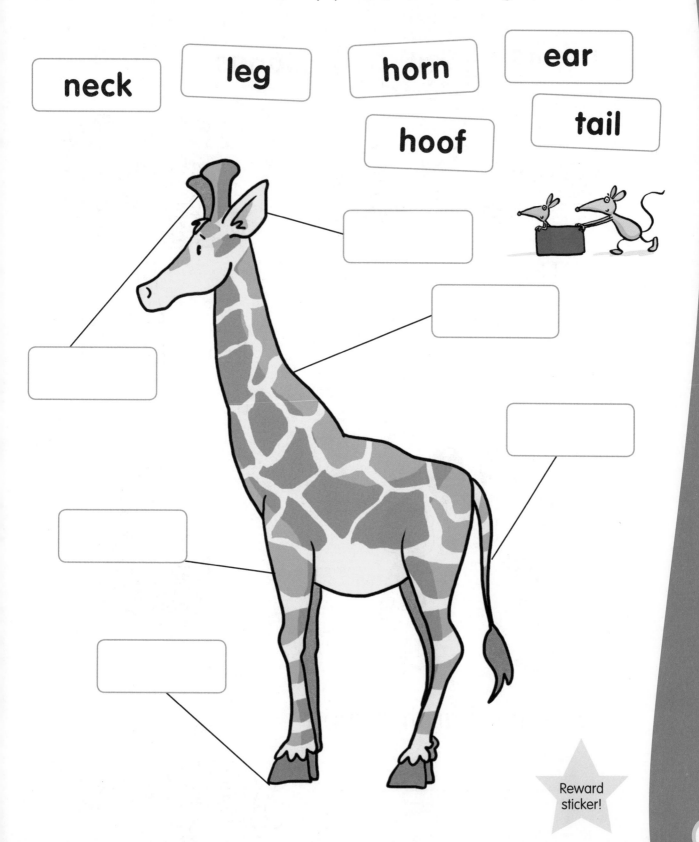

Reward sticker!

Reading and writing

Look at the pictures below. Under each one is a sentence with a word missing. Choose the correct word from the boxes below and write it in.

| books | cat | balloons | tree |

The _____ is chasing the dog.

Erin likes sitting in the _____.

Joe and Samir have

_____.

Jason loves

_____.

Reward sticker!

Reading and matching

Write the correct sentence beside each picture.

- The boys are carefully holding their balloons.
- The scared dog is being chased by a cat!
- Erin is hiding in the tall tree.
- Jason is quietly reading his book.

1. _____

_____

2. _____

_____

3. _____

_____

4. _____

Reward sticker!

Capital letters

Words that are the names of people or places are given **capital letters**. These words are called **proper nouns**. Look at the words below and circle the ones that should have capital letters.

computer

olivia

england

hippo

scotland

james

france

wales

apple

trees

bicycle

boat

book

carrot

fiona

Now look at the sentences below and circle the words that should have **capital letters**. Remember the first word of any sentence should also start with a capital letter.

a flag flutters in sean's hand.

julia would like to go to america.

surriya is going to pakistan to see her grandparents.

falling leaves and conkers remind chris of autumn.

the birds fly all the way to africa in winter.

Now write your own sentence using capital letters. Try to make sure it includes the name of a person and a place.

_____

_____

_____

Full stops

We finish sentences with a **full stop**. Arrange the words below into sentences, and add a full stop at the end of each one.

James football played

_____

Australia Kangaroos in live

_____

wet and cold is December

_____

Susan two brothers Jim and Niall called has

_____

Reward sticker!

It's your turn to be the teacher! Get a red pencil and put a circle around the letters that should have **capital letters** and write in the **full stops**.

1. "i like porridge," goldilocks muttered as she ran away

2. hippos and giraffes live in africa

3. if I lived at the north pole i might see father christmas

4. the capital city of england is london

5. james has 3 brothers: joseph, simon and peter. they live in bristol

6. the space rocket flew to jupiter

Reward sticker!

Question marks

We use **question marks** to show that we are asking something. Do you see that dot under the squiggle? A question mark goes at the end of a sentence instead of a full stop. Trace over the following question marks and finish the row.

? ? ?

Read the following sentences. Some are asking you something. You need to put a question mark after these ones. The others are statements. They tell you something and just need a full stop.

1. What is your favourite colour

2. I don't like ice cream

3. Birds fly through the air

4. Do you want to go to the park

5. Which cake would you like

6. Africa and Asia are both continents

Commas

We use **commas** for different reasons. One of the reasons is when we list things. Commas go in between the things in the list.
E.g. I went to the shop and I bought an apple, a banana, a pear and an orange. Don't forget to add **and** before the last item in the list.

Fill in the gaps with nouns (words for things).
Choose whatever you like!

I went to the shop and I bought a

_____, a _____

and a _____.

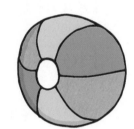

I went on holiday and I took a

_____, a _____

and a _____.

For my birthday I would like a

_____, a _____

and a _____.

Reward
sticker!

Punctuation

Read the passage. Write in the missing **commas** and circle any words that should have **capital letters**. Can you spot any questions that should be followed by a **question mark**? If so, put them in!

Susan put her hand in her bag

She was surprised to find a

book an apple and a big monkey.

How could they have got there

what else would she find

could the bag be magic

What would you expect to find in your school bag? Write a sentence below using capital letters and commas.

_____

_____

_____

Write a postcard

Imagine you are on holiday at the beach. Write a message to your friend to say what you are doing.

Today I went to the beach.

Comprehension

Read the Little Red Riding Hood story below and answer the questions on the opposite page.

1.

Little Red Riding Hood decided to visit her sick grandmother.

2.

When she was picking some flowers in the forest, she met a wolf.

3.

When Little Red Riding Hood arrived at the house, the wolf had dressed up as her grandmother.

4.

"My, what big teeth you have," said Little Red Riding Hood.
"All the better to eat you with!" cried the wolf.

Reward sticker!

5.

6.

The wolf leapt out of bed and jumped on poor Little Red Riding Hood.

Luckily, a woodcutter was passing by and rescued her from the wicked wolf.

1. Who was Little Red Riding Hood going to visit?

_____

2. Who did she meet in the forest?

_____

3. What was she doing when she met the wolf?

_____

4. Who did the wolf pretend to be?

_____

5. Who saved Little Red Riding Hood?

_____

Reward sticker!

Story-writing

Read the passage of text below. Write the next two sentences to continue the story. What do you think happens next?

Eli walked down the path, through the shaded trees. He could hear the birds singing. Eli wondered what the birds were saying. Then, he heard a voice saying, "Hello Eli!" Eli couldn't see anyone, so he walked on. Suddenly he heard a crunch on the path. He turned and there stood a bear. A small bear, wearing a hat and a pair of sunglasses. It waved, smiled and stepped slowly towards him.

_____

_____

_____

_____

Reward sticker!

Describe it

Some words help us to **describe** things, such as the **small** dog or the **sweet** apple. These words are called **adjectives**. Find the describing words below and circle them.

The small boy ate the big apple.

A fluffy cat sat in the red basket.

The dark clouds made the afternoon gloomy and dull.

The scary lion gave a loud roar and shook his

orange mane.

Now write your own sentence using as many **adjectives** as you can.

_____

_____

_____

Reward
sticker!

23

Descriptive writing

Describe the picture below in two sentences. Make sure that you use **adjectives** to make your writing more interesting.

_____

_____

_____

_____

Reward sticker!

Alphabetical order

Look at the words below. Put them in alphabetical order.
Then draw lines to join each word to the correct image.

a b c d e f g h i j k l m n o p q r s t u v w x y z

tent   mitten   witch   tree

lamp   clown   duck

_____

_____

_____

_____

_____

_____

Reward sticker!

25

Reading non-fiction

Read the passage below and answer the questions.

Giraffes are the tallest land animals. A giraffe could look into a second-floor window without even having to stand on its tiptoes! A giraffe's neck is 180 centimetres long. The legs of a giraffe are also 180 cm long. The back legs look shorter than the front legs, but they are actually about the same length.

Giraffes live in Africa. Some giraffes from Kenya have spots that are shaped like oak leaves. Some scientists think that the giraffe's pattern is for camouflage.

Both male and female giraffes have two hair-covered horns. Male giraffes use their horns to fight with one another. They are quite shy animals. Giraffes have blue-coloured tongues. This is because they eat a lot of leaves. They use their tongues to rip the leaves off the trees, so their tongues spend a long time in the sun. Because they are a blue colour, they don't get sunburnt!

Reward sticker!

1. What are the tallest land animals?

_____

2. How long is a giraffe's neck?

_____

3. Where do giraffes live?

_____

4. What type of leaves do the spots sometimes look like?

_____

5. How many horns does a giraffe have?

_____

6. What colour is a giraffe's tongue?

_____

7. How does this help giraffes?

_____

Reward sticker!

Roll up! Roll up!

Read this poster about a circus that is coming to town.

The Big Top Circus
presents

Fred the fearless fire-eater,
Justin the juggler,
Clive the crazy clown,
Tracey the trapeze artist,
Alan the acrobat
and lots, lots more.

Join us at the Big Top for a
fun-filled evening to remember!

Date: Saturday 3rd July
Time: 7pm **Place:** Woodside Park
Price: Adults £2.50   Children £1.75

Reward sticker!

Using the information from the poster, answer the questions below by putting a tick in the correct box.

1. What is the name of the circus?

☐ Small Top   ☐ Big Top

☐ Big Hat

2. What is Alan's job?

☐ An acrobat   ☐ A clown

☐ A juggler

3. Who is the trapeze artist?

☐ Tracey   ☐ Tara

☐ Alan

4. What time does the show start?

☐ 6pm   ☐ 7am

☐ 7pm

5. How much are tickets for children?

☐ £1.75   ☐ £2.20

☐ £17.50

Reward sticker!

More questions

Read the poster on page 28 again.
Now answer these questions.

1. Where is the circus being held?

_____

2. Why is Fred described as fearless?

_____

3. What else do you think you might see at the circus?

_____

4. Would you rather be a clown, a juggler,
a fire-eater or a trapeze artist?

_____

5. Why?

_____

_____

_____

Reward
sticker!

Writing practice

Can you make these sentences more interesting by adding detail and description?

E.g. The worm was in the earth ➔
The long, thin wriggly worm squirmed into the warm earth.

The leaves fell from the tree.

_____

_____

James bought a cake.

_____

_____

Answers:

Page 2: Alphabet blocks
ball, chair, drum, fork, tree, stamp,

Page 3: Finish the rhyme
four, ten, go, you, finger

Pages 6-7: Missing vowels
cat, bed, fan, dog, mug, hen, nut, box, king, flag, frog, drum, ship, harp, mast, swim

Page 8: Missing consonants
frog, tree, rocket, table, car, clock, sock, crab, brush

Page 9: Labels

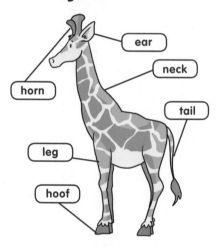

ear, neck, horn, tail, leg, hoof

Page 10: Reading and writing
cat, tree, balloons, books

Page 11: Reading and matching
1. The scared dog is being chased by a cat!
2. Jason is quietly reading his book.
3. The boys are carefully holding their balloons.
4. Erin is hiding in the tall tree.

Pages 12-13: Capital letters
Olivia, England, Scotland, James, France, Wales, Fiona

A flag flutters in Sean's hand.
Julia would like to go to America.
Surriya is going to Pakistan to see her grandparents.
Falling leaves and conkers remind Chris of autumn.
The birds fly all the way to Africa in winter.

Pages 14-15: Full stops
James played football.
Kangaroos live in Australia.
December is cold and wet.
Susan has two brothers called Jim and Niall.

1. "I like porridge," Goldilocks muttered as she ran away.
2. Hippos and giraffes live in Africa.
3. If I lived at the North Pole I might see Father Christmas.
4. The capital city of England is London.
5. James has 3 brothers: Joseph, Simon and Peter. They live in Bristol.
6. The space rocket flew to Jupiter.

Page 16: Question marks
1. What is your favourite colour?
2. I don't like ice cream.
3. Birds fly through the air.
4. Do you want to go to the park?
5. Which cake would you like?
6. Africa and Asia are both continents.

Page 18: Punctuation
Susan put her hand in her bag. She was surprised to find a book, an apple and a big monkey. How could they have got there? What else would she find? Could the bag be magic?

Pages 20-21: Comprehension
1. She was visiting her sick grandmother.
2. She met a wolf.
3. She was picking some flowers.
4. The wolf pretended to be her grandmother.
5. A woodcutter saved her.

Page 23: Describe it
The small boy ate the big apple.
A fluffy cat sat in the red basket.
The dark clouds made the afternoon gloomy and dull.
The scary lion gave a loud roar and shook his orange mane.

Page 25: Alphabetical order
clown, duck, lamp, mitten, tent, tree, witch

Pages 26-27: Reading non-fiction
1. Giraffes are the tallest land animal.
2. A giraffe's neck is 180 centimetres.
3. Giraffes live in Africa.
4. The spots are sometimes shaped like oak leaves.
5. Giraffes have two horns.
6. Giraffes have blue tongues.
7. They don't get sunburnt.

Pages 28-29: Roll up! Roll up!
1. Big Top.
2. An acrobat.
3. Tracey.
4. 7pm.
5. £1.75.

Page 30: More questions
1. The circus is being held at Woodside Park.
2. He eats fire.
3. Example answers: tightrope walker, ringmaster, strongman